A Bouquet of *LITTLES*

By

RUTH KRAUSS

Pictures by

JANE FLORA

HARPER & ROW, PUBLISHERS

NEW YORK, EVANSTON, AND LONDON

A BOUQUET OF LITTLES

Text copyright © 1963 by Ruth Krauss
Pictures copyright © 1963 by Jane Flora
All rights reserved.

A Bouquet of
LITTLES

to Robert Herrick

A little shell best fits a little egg,
A little pull best fits a little leg,
As my small please best fits my little beg.

a little door best fits a little bell
a little sea best fits a little shell

A little gleam best fits a little eye,
A little sad best fits a little sigh,
As my small moon best fits my little sky.

a little street best fits a little lamp
a little lick best fits a little stamp

A little foot best fits a little kick,
A little bricklayer fits a little brick,
As my small tock best fits my little tick.

a little backyard fits a little alley
a little mountain fits a little valley

A little duck best fits a little quack,
A little earthquake fits a little crack,
As my small spud best fits my little sack.

a little give best fits a little take
a little swan best fits a little lake

a little dance best fits a little shake

A little rug best fits a little floor,
A little storeman fits a little store,
As my small sea best fits my little roar.

a little dust best fits a little mop
a little badge best fits a little cop

a little storm best fits a little thunder
a little Alice fits a little wonder

A little shine best fits a little sun,
A little raisin fits a little bun,
As my small road best fits my little run.

a little king best fits a little land
a little park best fits a little band

A little town best fits a little dump,
A little camel fits a little hump,
As my small ouch! best fits my little bump.

a little meek best fits a little mild
a little whoop! whoop! whoop! best fits a little wild

a little wood best fits a little fawn
a little cobweb fits a little dawn

a little onion fits a little stew
a little cobweb fits a little dew

A little skirt best fits a little lace,
A little monkey fits a little face,
As my small catch best fits my little chase.

a little stew best fits a little pot
a little polka fits a little dot

a little Beauty fits a little Beast
a little table fits a little feast

A little bell best fits a little ring,
A little bee best fits a little sting,
As my small branch best fits my little swing.

a little la la la best fits a little sing

a little here best fits a little there.
a little fountain fits a little square

A little water fits a little well
a little blue best fits a little bell
a little word best fits a little spell
a little roar best fits a little shell

as sweetly now, my small farewell

a little hole best fits a little mending
a little start best fits a little ending